TABLE OF CONTENTS

INTRODUCING . . .

VICTOR FRANKENSTEIN

ELIZABETH

MR FRANKENSTEIN

ROBERT
WALTON
THE MONSTER

CHAPTER ONE:

MYSTERY ON THE ICE

Somewhere near the Arctic Circle, in the late 1700s, a Russian ship is trapped in the ice.

Robert Walton, the English captain, was nervous.

We can't move.
The ice is too thick.
We'll never reach the
North Pole!

What the–?
Is something wrong, Captain?
Look at this.
I don't believe it! Something is out there. And it's coming closer!
That was no thing. That was a man! And he was enormous! I've never seen anything like it.

The sailors watched as the dark figure seemed to approach the ship. Then it turned and moved into the distance.

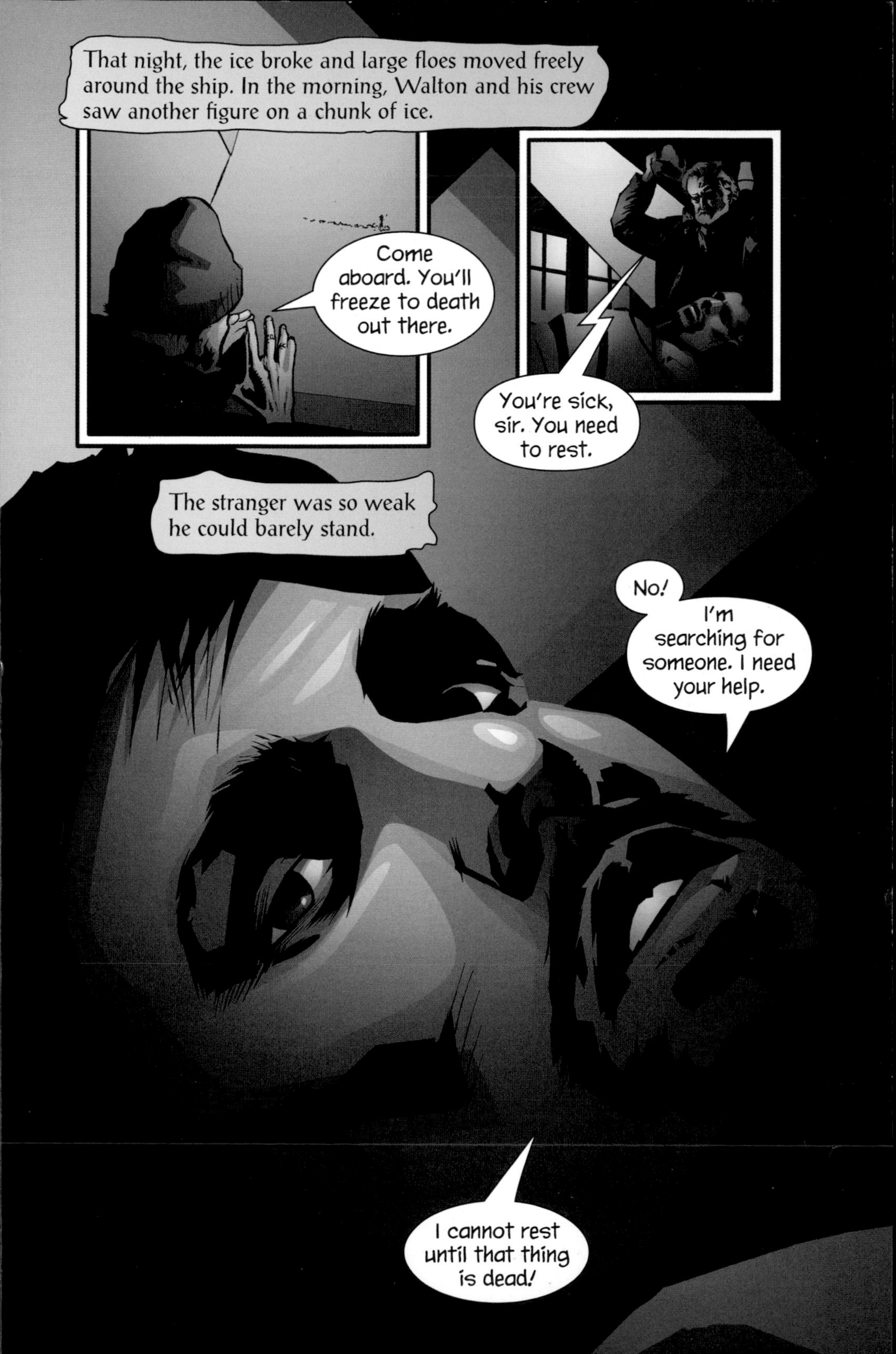

That night, the ice broke and large floes moved freely around the ship. In the morning, Walton and his crew saw another figure on a chunk of ice.

You're sick, sir. You need to rest.

The stranger was so weak he could barely stand.

No! I'm searching for someone. I need your help.

I cannot rest until that thing is dead!

Captain, you think he's looking for that figure we saw on the ice?
Walton explained about the dark figure the crew had seen the day before. The stranger grew excited with every word he heard.
What did you see?
Tell me! It must have been that hideous creature!
That's him! He's out there. I must find him!
All right, sir, we'll help you. But first you must rest.

The next morning, Walton returned to the stranger's bed.
My name's Walton. We're hoping to reach the North Pole.
So, you want to understand the unknown.
I was like you once, excited to learn all I could. Until . . .
Until I went too far.
My name is Victor Frankenstein. That creature on the ice is the reason I'm here.
This is what happened . . .

Chapter Two:
The Dead Come Back to Life

My story begins in Geneva, Switzerland, where I was born. As a boy, I was curious about the world.
I wanted to know everything. In my father's library, I discovered many interesting books. I shared them with my best friend, Henry Clerval.
This book says humans can call forth ghosts and devils.
That's crazy, Victor. No one can do that.
The alchemists say there is a potion that can make us live forever.

I studied the alchemists' writings for several years. But then a new interest grabbed me. It came during a thunderstorm.

CRAACKKKK!

What power there is in a single bolt of lightning!
I soon learned about electricity from my father's friend. I lost interest in the alchemists. Now I would study real science.

At age 17, I went to college in Germany. After two years of hard work, a question popped into my mind. What creates life?
To answer that question, I thought, I must first explore death.
This graveyard should provide some answers.
I took the bones and flesh I found back to my apartment. Soon, I made a great discovery.

I have done it!
I have brought dead matter back to life!
Still, I needed to do more!
So I returned to the graveyard.
What on earth do you want all this for?
Never mind. Will you sell it to me or not?

Finally, I had assembled all the material I needed for my plan.
What are you doing in that house of yours?
None of your business.
He's a great scientist, too good for simple students like us.
From dead skin and bones, I would create a living being. Electricity would bring it to life. And my creature would treat me as if I were a god. The work, however, took time.
They make fun of me now. But wait until they see my creation!

After months of putting together a body, I was almost done.

Must finish tonight. Can't go on like this.

At last! Everything is ready.

Now!

CRAACKKK!

I've done it!
It's alive!
But then my excitement turned to terror. What had I done? I had given life to what had been dead! What horrors had I created?

I ran into my bedroom next door. The creature did not stir. I tried to sleep, but my head filled with horrible pictures.
It's too awful, it's all–
AAAARRRRGH.
No!
Get away!

I fled down the stairs and outside into the yard. My heart pounded in my chest as I waited for the monster.
But there was nothing.
By the morning, the skies had cleared. I headed into the city.
Victor!
Henry? What are you doing here?
I've come to visit you, of course. I haven't heard from you in a while.
You look awful, Victor. So tired.
Yes.
I've been quite busy.

Come on. You must rest. Let's go to your house.
My house?
I tried to delay, but Henry insisted.
Okay, Henry, but let me go first.
He's gone!
Thank goodness he's gone.

CHAPTER THREE:
DEATH IN THE FAMILY

During my trip to Switzerland, I could only think about my poor younger brother. Just before reaching home . . .
Did you see that?
What? I didn't see a thing.
Never mind. It must have been my imagination.
I didn't tell Henry, but I knew I had seen my monster. Why had he come here?

The next morning, I was finally home. I hugged my father and Elizabeth, a childhood friend. Elizabeth and I had written often while I was at school. We had hoped to be married soon.
We're so glad you're home, Victor. William's death was so awful.
It is too terrible for words.
The police say they have captured the killer.
Father, who is it?
They say it was Justine.
The police are wrong!

Justine had moved in with my family while I was away. She was a sweet and harmless child. I knew she could not have killed William. In an instant, I knew my monster had done it.

They found her with William's locket. She could not explain how she got it.

Anger and hatred boiled inside me. Somehow I knew my monster had killed William. Now, Justine would also die, thanks to that beast. Because I had created him, I was responsible for two deaths!
What will you do next, you monstrous thing? I will do anything to destroy you!
Anything!

A few months later, the deaths of William and Justine weighed heavily on me. I needed to be alone. I set off for the mountains of France, where I had travelled once before.
It's so peaceful here.
What the . . . what's that?

It can't be!

You! You devil!
I should destroy you this instant!
Hatred filled my body. Then, to my horrified surprise . . .

I am a horrible being, but you made me. Do me one favour, and I will leave you alone forever.
No! I'll kill—
SMACK!
I am too fast and strong. You can't harm me. And I won't harm you, if . . .
If what?
If you do what I ask.

I was not evil when you made me.
The humans I met hated me and tried to kill me. They have made me an angry creature.

And a lonely one.

I wish I could forget that night I gave you life.
Listen to me! Hear what I have seen and what I have done.

If my words don't change your mind, then you can have what you desire.

I will let you destroy me.

I have a hut up in the mountains. Come with me.

The monster disgusted me, but he was my creation. I owed him something. And I was curious to hear about what he had done since that night in my house. I agreed to follow him up to the mountain.

Sit. And listen to my tale. Listen to how I became what I am.

Before I left your house, I took some of your clothes. Then I went into the woods. I was like a newborn baby. I could move, but I knew nothing about the world. I looked for food to eat. I slept outside, in the cold and the rain.
Then one day, I came to a cottage in a small village.
Ahhh! Mummy, help!
Get away! Get away from my children!

Help! Help us!
That thing tried to attack my family!
Hurry, men! There's trouble over there!
Go away!
Leave us alone!
Later, I saw myself in a pool of water. I looked so different from the villagers. Now I knew why they chased me. To them, I was a monster.

In a little while, I came to a cottage near a field. Right behind it was a shed. I hid inside. Through a hole in the wooden walls, I could see directly into the cottage.

I watched the family for many weeks.

From them, I learned my first words. I saw that they were poor, and I felt sad for them.
Felix, Where did this firewood come from?
It's like some ghost or spirit is watching over us.

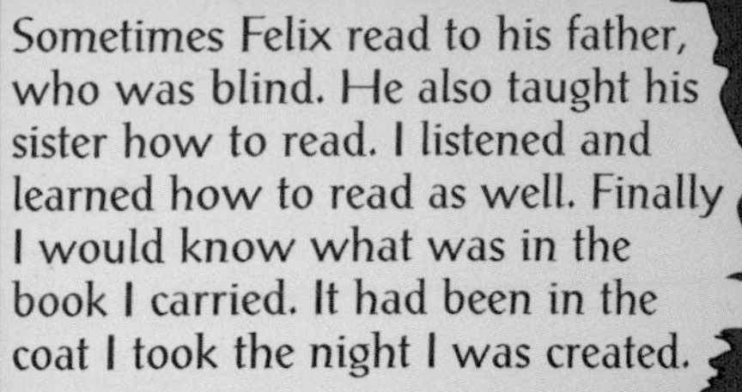

Sometimes Felix read to his father, who was blind. He also taught his sister how to read. I listened and learned how to read as well. Finally I would know what was in the book I carried. It had been in the coat I took the night I was created.

"I, Victor Frankenstein, have found a way to bring dead matter to life."

This man Frankenstein is my creator.

And even he thought I was an ugly, monstrous thing!

I decided the time had come to make friends. I waited for Agatha and Felix to leave, then knocked at the door.
Who is it?
I am a traveller, sir. I just wanted to rest here for–
Ahhhh!
You demon!
Let him go!
No, please–
WHAM!
Ugh!

I could have crushed the boy with one hand. Instead, I ran off into the woods.

You monster! Leave us alone!

I knew from your journal, Frankenstein, where you lived. I decided to track you down. Only you could end my suffering.

I travelled for months. On a beautiful spring day, I stopped to rest by a small stream. I was not alone.

But now I was the one in danger.
Get away from her.
But I–
BANG!
It took several weeks for me to recover from my wound. I kept thinking about all the pain humans had caused me.

I continued my journey. Just outside Geneva, I met a small boy. I thought perhaps he could be my friend.

Hello, child. Please, listen to me.

An ogre! You want to eat me! Get away!

I won't harm you. Please!

Stop! My father is Mr. Frankenstein, and he'll get the police after you.

Frankenstein? You are a Frankenstein?

You are my enemy!

The boy struggled only for a moment.
I found a locket on the boy's body, so I took it.
Then I headed for the city. Along the way, I saw a barn. Inside the barn, I saw a young woman sleeping. Seeing her gave me an idea.
Let her take the blame for the murder.

Soon after I left the barn I met you. And now you know my story.

You killed my brother and played a part in Justine's death.

I will do worse, if you won't help me.

You must create a female, just like me.

Create another monster like you, so you can destroy the world?
Never!
If I had a woman like me, she would know what it was like to be hideous.
She would feel the way I feel. And then I would not feel so alone.

The monster's words made sense to me. I knew the damage he could do others if he remained angry at me and the world.
All right. I'll do it.
Thank you, Frankenstein!
But when I finish, you two must go off into the wild and never bother humans again.
Yes, yes, anything you say.

CHAPTER FOUR:

I left the monster's hut and returned home. To keep my promise and build a second creature, I went to England. The scientists there had done work that could help me with my new project.

Leaving again?

But you just got back.

I know, Father. But this work is important. I must go.

We will be married as soon as I return. Is that all right?
Of course, Victor.
But Victor, please be careful.

As I hurried to England . . .
The monster is out there, following me.
He watches everything I do.
I finally arrived back at the graveyard, where this horrible nightmare first began.
There you go, sir. All the muscles and organs you asked for.
Thank you.

I then headed north to Scotland, to a distant island. I wanted to be far from other people while I did my horrible task. I rented a cottage and began to work.
The months passed . . .
She is almost ready.
But what if she is even more awful than the first? What if she refuses to go with the monster?
This is wrong!
She must be destroyed!

What was that?

Victor, what are you doing?!

No! Stop!

My hands trembled, and anger rose up inside me.

All I could think about was the pain the monster had brought to me and my family.

SLAM!

SMASH!

Very well.

You have made your decision. And you will pay for it.

You have robbed me of my wedding night.

So I will be with you on yours!

With those words, the monster fled the cottage.
The beast means to kill me after I marry Elizabeth!
I took my time returning to Switzerland. Over and over in my mind I saw the beast coming for me. Perhaps I could kill him, then Elizabeth and I would be free to live our lives in peace.
It's so good to see you.
Victor, you don't look well. Are you all right?
I'm fine. Everything's fine.

On our wedding day, I tried to act as joyful as I could.
I'm so happy, Victor.
Are you?
Victor?
Elizabeth looked so beautiful, and I tried to hide the dread inside me.
Of course, my dear. I have never been happier.
But I couldn't forget what the monster had said.
I will be with you on your wedding night!

CHAPTER FIVE:

THE END OF FRANKENSTEIN

We travelled for several hours until we reached the hotel where we would spend our honeymoon.

Oh, how lovely. It looks so peaceful.

Let's hope it remains that way.

Victor, are you ill?
Is something wrong?
Everything's fine. Go to bed.
Elizabeth stayed in the room while I went outside to look for the monster. I wanted to find him before he found me. But I saw no sign of him.

After an hour, I returned to the room.
Ahhh!
Elizabeth!
You broke your promise, but I kept mine!

Stop!
The monster ran from the hotel and faded into the blackness. All I could think about was stopping my creation before he killed again.

But first I had to bury my poor Elizabeth.
I will have revenge, Elizabeth. I will track him down, or die trying!
All right then, catch me if you can!
It's YOU!
The monster raced off, and I ran after him.

For months I followed the monster over land and sea. He travelled northward. I bought a dogsled and followed his trail onto a frozen sea.

There!
There he is!

The ice!

No! He's getting away!

After drifting for several hours, I realized my little island of ice was melting. I would soon sink into the freezing waters. But then . . .
Come aboard, sir. You'll freeze to death out there.
And that, Captain Walton, is how you came to find me.
Amazing!
You don't believe me. Even though you saw the creature yourself, Captain.
I did see something . . .

For several days, Victor Frankenstein battled fever and sickness . . .
I owed him some happiness.
I created him, and then I left him alone in a cruel world.
You did the right thing.
Captain, there are some things humans should never attempt.
With those words, Walton felt Victor's body go limp and die.
Walton left the cabin, to arrange for Victor's burial.

An hour later, he returned.

Who are you?

He is dead because of me. He is my last victim!

He did not deserve to die like this.

Now there is only one death left.
Mine.
I will go far away and kill myself.
No one will ever remember Frankenstein's monster!

ABOUT MARY SHELLEY

Mary Wollstonecraft Godwin was born 30 August, 1797, in London. Her parents were both writers, but sadly, her mother died while Mary was a baby. After being taught at home as a child, Mary fell in love at a young age. At 16, she married Percy Shelley and changed her name to Mary Shelley. In 1816, the couple travelled to Switzerland for the summer. While there, Shelley and other writers decided to have a ghost story contest. Shelley started writing *Frankenstein.* Published in 1818, the novel still frightens people nearly 200 years later.

ABOUT THE RETELLING AUTHOR

Michael Burgan has written more than 90 fiction and non-fiction books for children. A history graduate from the University of Connecticut, USA, Burgan worked at *Weekly Reader* for six years before beginning his freelance career. He has received an award from the Educational Press Association of America and has won several playwriting contests. He lives in Chicago, USA with his wife, Samantha.

ABOUT THE ILLUSTRATOR

Dennis Calero has illustrated book covers, comic books, and role-playing games for more than ten years. He's worked for companies such as Marvel, DC, White Wolf, and Wizards of the Coast. Dennis is currently illustrating a series of Conan the Barbarian lithographs.

GLOSSARY

alchemists (AL-kem-ists) - persons who practise the ancient science known as **alchemy** (AL-kem-ee). These scientists seek to turn metal into gold, discover a cure for disease, and develop medicine for people to live forever.

Arctic Circle (ARK-tik SUR-kuhl) - an area circling the northern part of the earth, where temperatures are extremely cold

cottage (KOT-ij) - a small house in the country

dogsled (DAWG-sled) - a sled pulled by dogs, used for travelling over ice and snow

floes (FLOWZ) - large sheets of floating ice

hideous (HID-ee-uhss) - horribly ugly

locket (LOK-it) - a small piece of jewellery that usually hangs from a necklace and can hold a photograph or other small item

ogre (OH-gur) - an ugly giant in fairy tales that feeds on human beings

potion (POH-shuhn) - a mixture of liquids

victim (VIK-tuhm) - a person that is injured or killed

FRANKENSTEIN FACTS!

The idea for *Frankenstein* came from a dream! One night in 1816, Mary Shelley and other authors decided to have a ghost story contest. At first, Shelley couldn't think of an idea. That evening, however, she dreamed about a frightening monster. The next day, she started writing her famous novel.

Shelley wasn't the only author in the ghost story contest to create a famous monster. John Polidori started writing a book called *The Vampyre.* Even today, most vampires are modelled after Polidori's version.

In 1818, the first edition of *Frankenstein* was published in three parts and didn't include Shelley's name. The author's name didn't appear on the cover until the second edition, published in 1823.

Many people who have not read the book believe that Shelley named her monster Frankenstein. In fact, she never gave the monster a name.

The first film about the Frankenstein monster was shown in 1910. Like other films during this time, the movie didn't have any sound. It was also only 12 minutes long.

Many people imagine Frankenstein's monster with bolts in his neck, stitches across his forehead, and green skin. Actually, the monster's looks have changed many times. The image often used on Halloween masks became famous in 1931. That year, actor Boris Karloff played the monster in the movie *Frankenstein*.

In Mary Shelley's book, Victor Frankenstein destroys the monster's wife. In the 1935 sequel to the *Frankenstein* movie, the scientist decides to grant the monster's wish. The *Bride of Frankenstein* quickly became another horror film classic.

Since *The Bride of Frankenstein* movie, the Frankenstein monster has starred in hundreds of other films, TV shows, and comic books. Today, Shelley's creation continues to frighten people of all ages.

DISCUSSION QUESTIONS

1. Do you think Frankenstein's monster was evil? Why do you think he did such bad things?

2. People feared Frankenstein's monster because of the way he looked. How did this make the monster feel? Have you ever treated someone differently based on their looks?

3. Victor Frankenstein destroys the monster's wife before she comes to life. What do you think would have happened if the monster's wife had lived? Do you think the ending would have been happier?

WRITING PROMPTS

1. Create your own super animal! Pick three different body parts from three different animals, such as a giraffe's neck, a gorilla's body, and a shark's teeth. Then pick a name for your animal, such as Girillark, and write a story about it.

2. Victor Frankenstein chased the monster almost as far as the North Pole. What do you think would have happened if he had caught the creature? Write down your ideas.

3. At the end of the story, Frankenstein's monster says that he will destroy himself. Do you believe him? If he doesn't destroy himself, what do you think he would do instead? Write a new ending to the story.

OTHER BOOKS

DRACULA

On a business trip to Transylvania, Jonathan Harker stays at an eerie castle owned by a man named Count Dracula. When strange things start to happen, Harker investigates and finds the count sleeping in a coffin! Harker isn't safe, and when the count escapes to London, neither are his friends.

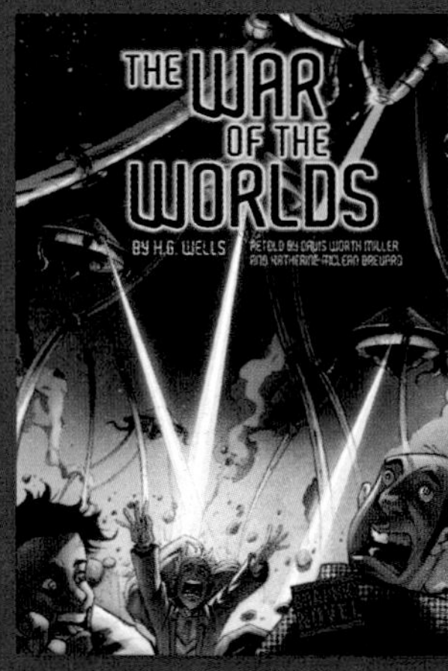

THE WAR OF THE WORLDS

In the late 19th century, a cylinder crashes down near London. When George investigates, a Martian activates an evil machine and begins destroying everything in its path! George must find a way to survive a War of the Worlds.

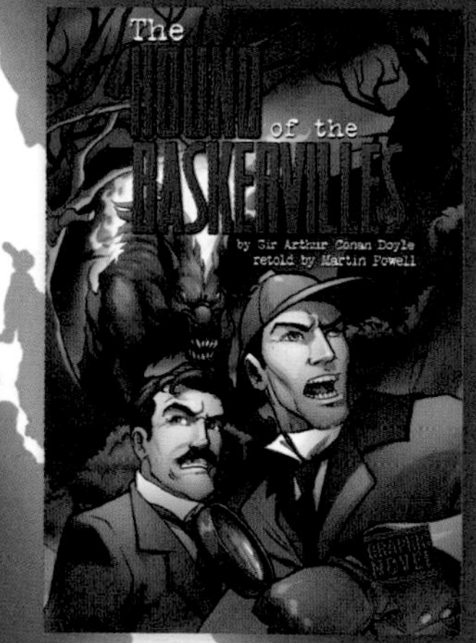

THE HOUND OF THE BASKERVILLES

Late one night, Sir Charles Baskerville is attacked outside his castle in Dartmoor, Devon. Could it be the Hound of the Baskervilles, a legendary creature that haunts the nearby moor? Sherlock Holmes, the world's greatest detective, is on the case.

TREASURE ISLAND

Jim Hawkins had no idea what he was getting into when the pirate Billy Bones showed up at the doorstep of his mother's inn. When Billy dies suddenly, Jim is left to unlock his old sea chest, which reveals money, a journal, and a treasure map. Joined by a band of honourable men, Jim sets sail on a dangerous voyage to locate the loot on a faraway island. The violent sea is only one of the dangers they face. They soon encounter a band of bloodthirsty pirates determined to make the treasure their own!

GRAPHIC REVOLVE

If you have enjoyed this story, there are many more exciting tales for you to discover in the Graphic Revolve collection...

20,000 Leagues Under the Sea

Black Beauty

Dracula

Frankenstein

Gulliver's Travels

The Hound of the Baskervilles

The Hunchback of Notre Dame

King Arthur and the Knights of the Round Table

Robin Hood

The Strange Case of Dr Jekyll and Mr Hyde

Treasure Island

The War of the Worlds